Care & Compassion

Old Prints and Photographs of Hospitals and Nurses in Berkshire and South Oxfordshire 1839-1930

Compiled by Margaret Railton and Marshall Barr for The Berkshire Medical Heritage Centre

ISBN 0 9539417 0 1

Typeset in 10.5/14 Fenice Light
Graphic design by The Harper Partnership
Printed by MRM Associates Limited, Reading

CONTENTS

ACKNOWLEDGEMENTS

Many people have helped with the compilation of this booklet. In particular we thank Mr Lionel Williams and Mr Bryan Miles for the endless trouble they have taken in obtaining the images and scans ready for printing and Mr Chris Harper of the Harper Partnership for his ingenuity with the design and layout.

We thank the following people and organisations for giving us information and allowing us to reproduce prints and photographs from their archives:
The Royal Berkshire and Battle Hospitals NHS Trust, Heatherwood and Wexham Park Hospitals Trust, Mr Jason Canlin, West Berkshire Priority Services NHS Trust, East Berkshire Community Health NHS Trust, Mrs Alison Rees, East Berkshire NHS Trust, Mr Paul Robertson and Mr John Heritage of the Broadmoor Hospital Authority, Dr Peter Durrant and the staff of the Berkshire County Record Office, Mrs Caroline Benson (Rural History Centre, University of Reading), Mrs Nuala La Vertue (Oxfordshire Photographic Archive), Mr Alan Hankin (Reading Local Studies Library), Mr Javier Pes (Reading Museum Service), Mr Paul Cannon (West Berkshire Heritage Service), Mrs Vicky Mohammed (Slough Museum), Dr Judith Hunter (Royal Borough Collection), Mrs Judy Dewey and Miss Daphne Baker (Wallingford Museum), Mrs Joyce Sampson (Clewer Parish Church Local History Museum), The Mother Superior and Sister Pamela, Convent of St John the Baptist, Clewer, Mrs Pat Curtis (Maidenhead Library), Mrs Penny Overd (Ascot Heath Library), Mrs Carol Carson (Wokingham Library), Mrs Netty Bradbury (Windsor Library), Mrs M Aldridge, Mr David Beasley, Mr John Bond, Revd Valerie Bonham, Mr Brian Boulter, Mr Bryan Brinkley, Miss Cook, Mr Richard Dove, Mrs Hilary Fisher, Mr Sidney Gold, Mrs Eric Griffin, Mrs Sue Hopson, Revd Sebastian Jones, Miss Harriet Lucking, Mrs Iris Moon, Mr Luke Over, Mr Graham Parlour, Lady Pedler, Mrs Brenda Pither, Mr John Pither, Miss Pratt, Mrs Adele Sale, Mr Roy Scott, Mr and Mrs Roy Sheppard, Mrs Betty Southgate, Mr Peter Southwell, Mr A Stevens, Mrs Barbara Stoney, Mrs Ruth Timbrell, Mrs Jean Tyler, Mr C Walton, Miss Kathy Wheelan, Mr Lionel Williams, Mr K Woollacott, Mr W Wright.

PHOTOGRAPHS AND PRINTS (numbered) reproduced by courtesy of:
Rural History Centre, University of Reading: 1, 51, 58, 106, 109, 112, 115.
Royal Berkshire Hospital Archives: 2, 3, 4, 12, 14, 15, 16, 87, 88, 99, 100, 101, 102, 103, 113, 114, 126, 135, 138, 139, 151.
Mrs M Aldridge: 5, 7, 8, 9, 10.
Oxfordshire County Council Photographic Archive: 6, 54.
Mr W Wright: 11, 13.
Mrs M Railton: 17, 43, 68, 70, 74, 77, 79, 80, 81, 90, 105, 110, 128, 129, 130, 131, 132, 133, 142, 143, 146, 152.
Mrs B Southgate: 18, 19.
Newbury Hospital Archives: 20, 21, 22, 23, 24, 25, 140.

King Edward VII Hospital Archives: 26, 27, 28, 29, 30, 31, 32, 33, 34, 35, 36, 37, 141.
Mrs Eric Griffin: 38.
Mr David Beasley: 39, 40, 41, 42, 93, 107.
Mrs H Fisher: 44, 61, 62, 63, 64, 65, 66, 67, 69.
Mr John Pither: 45, 46.
Townlands Hospital Archives: 47.
Broadmoor Hospital Authority Archives / Illustrated London News Picture Library: 48, 49, 50.
Broadmoor Hospital Authority Archives: 52, 53.
Reading Local Studies Library: 55, 111, 127.
Mrs J Dewey: 56, 57.
Lady Pedler: 59.
Mr C Walton: 60.
West Berkshire Heritage Service: 71.
Mrs Sue Hopson / Rural History Centre, University of Reading: 72.
Heatherwood Hospital Archives: 73, 75, 76.
Mrs Ruth Timbrell: 78.
Mr Bryan Brinkley: 82.
The Mother Superior, Convent of St John the Baptist, Clewer: 83, 84, 85, 86.
Mrs Iris Moon / Rural History Centre, University of Reading: 89.
Reading Evening Post: 91.
Miss K Wheelan: 92.
Clewer Parish Church Local History Museum: 94.
Mr Brian Boulter: 95.
Mr Roy Scott: 96.
Slough Museum: 97, 118.
Mr A Stevens: 98.
Mr Martin Barrett / Slough Museum: 104.
Mr K Woollacott: 108.
Mr Lionel Williams: 116, 117, 119, 120, 121, 122, 123, 124, 125.
Mr Graham Parlour: 134, 137, 147, 148, 149.
Mr Roy Sheppard: 136, 150.
Mr Peter Southwell: 144, 145.

Front cover:
Photograph: Children's Ward, Royal Berkshire Hospital c1900. Mr A Stevens.
Background map: Reading and Surrounding District, 1842. Reading Local Studies Library.

INTRODUCTION

The Victorian period was an important time for hospital building and expansion. Voluntary hospitals, administered by Boards of Management, were built and maintained by donations and subscriptions. Patients were admitted by ticket on the recommendation of a subscriber and attended by honorary physicians and surgeons. No payment was required - both treatment and maintenance were free.

The formation of the Poor Law Unions in 1834 led to the construction of new workhouses, built and maintained by local rates. Most workhouses had their own infirmaries where pauper patients were attended by salaried medical officers appointed by the Boards of Guardians.

The need to isolate infectious cases and to provide specialised treatment produced more hospitals. By 1900 15 hospitals and 11 workhouses had been built in Berkshire (taking the 1974 boundaries) and South Oxfordshire. Between 1900 and 1930 a further 8 hospitals were opened.

In the meantime, as the importance of good nursing became recognised, arrangements were made to train and supply nurses to work in the community. Private nurses were trained by the Royal Berkshire Hospital in Reading from 1873. By the early 1900s Queen Victoria Nurses and Princess Christian Nurses had become well-known throughout the area. Local Nursing Associations were formed and the role of the district nurse and midwife became established.

When the Poor Law system ended in 1930 Union Workhouses became either Municipal Hospitals or Public Assistance Institutions (PAI) which cared for the elderly and chronic sick. In 1948 these former workhouses were integrated into the National Health Service with the voluntary and specialist hospitals.

Maternity homes have not been included in this booklet. Dellwood, opened in 1920 as a maternity home for Reading Borough, is the only one which later became a hospital. It is now a community hospital and part of the West Berkshire Priority Care Services NHS Trust. No pre-1930 photographs of Dellwood have been found.

Smallpox hospitals have also been excluded. By 1933 the success of vaccination led to the closure of all smallpox hospitals in Berkshire with the exception of Whitley Smallpox Hospital in Reading which was rebuilt to cater for all cases in Berkshire. Whitelands, in Henley, which served the South Oxfordshire area, closed in 1952. Whitley was closed in 1959 and the land sold for building.

After 1930 no further hospitals were built in the area until 1966 when Wexham Park Hospital was opened. Since 1948 out of the 34 hospitals built before 1930, 20 have been closed and the organisation and administration of the remaining 14 have been changed considerably.

This booklet of old prints and photographs shows some of these older hospitals built before 1930, their nursing staff and the forerunners of the district nurses. Unfortunately it is not comprehensive as many pre-1930 photographs have not survived and isolation hospitals and workhouses were seldom photographed. The accompanying map shows the location of the various hospitals in the area.

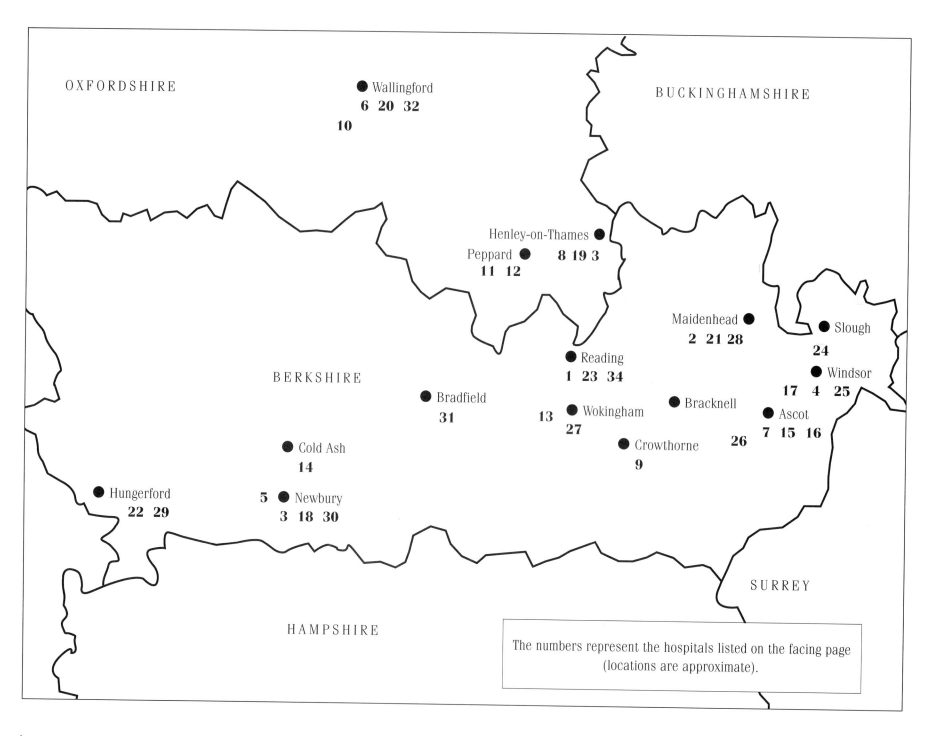

OXFORDSHIRE

BUCKINGHAMSHIRE

● Wallingford
6 20 32
10

Henley-on-Thames ●
Peppard ●   **8 19 3**
11 12

Maidenhead ●
2 21 28

● Slough
24

● Reading
1 23 34

BERKSHIRE

● Windsor
17   4   25

● Bradfield
31

13 ● Wokingham
27

● Bracknell

● Ascot
7 15 16

26

● Crowthorne
9

● Cold Ash
14

5 ● Newbury
3 18 30

● Hungerford
22 29

SURREY

HAMPSHIRE

The numbers represent the hospitals listed on the facing page
(locations are approximate).

HOSPITALS BUILT IN BERKSHIRE AND SOUTH OXFORDSHIRE BY 1930

1   Royal Berkshire Hospital, Reading - opened 1839

2   Maidenhead General Hospital - opened 1879 - closed 1977

3   Newbury District Hospital - opened 1885

4   King Edward VII Hospital, Windsor - opened 1909

5   Speen Cottage Hospital - opened 1869 - closed 1946

6   Wallingford Cottage Hospital - opened 1881- transferred to new premises 1929 - Community Hospital 1973

7   Royal Victoria Cottage Hospital, Ascot - opened 1898 - closed 1950s

8   Henley War Memorial Hospital - opened 1923 - closed 1984

9   Broadmoor Hospital, Crowthorne - opened 1863

10 Berkshire County Mental Hospital, Cholsey - opened 1870

11 Borocourt Hospital - opened 1930 - closed 1993

12 Peppard Sanatorium - opened 1898 - closed 1980s

13 Pinewood Sanatorium - opened 1901 - closed 1966

14 Cold Ash Children's Hospital - opened 1886 - closed 1963

15 Heatherwood Hospital - opened 1923 - after 1948 became a general hospital

16 London and Ascot Convalescent Hospital - opened 1863 - after 1948 became a private nursing home

17 St Andrew's Convalescent Hospital, Clewer - opened 1866 - closed for patients 1945 - demolished 1954

18 Wash Common Isolation Hospital, Newbury - opened 1893 - closed 1946*

19 Smith Hospital, Henley - opened 1892 - coverted to child psychiatric hospital 1952 - closed 1988 - sold 1990s*

20 Wallingford Isolation Hospital - opened 1904 - used for maternity cases c1950, demolished 1980s

21 Maidenhead Isolation Hospital - opened 1893 - used for respite cases 1978, closed 1984 - sold mid-1980s

22 Hungerford Isolation Hospital - opened early 1900s - demolished 1940s

23 Park Hospital, Reading - opened 1906 - closed for patients 1987, used for administrative headquarters

Former Workhouses

24 Upton Hospital, former Eton Union Workhouse

25 Old Windsor Hospital, former Windsor Union Workhouse closed in 1988, sold and converted into flats

26 Church Hill House Hospital, former Easthampstead Workhouse

27 Wokingham Hospital, former Wokingham Union Workhouse

28 St Mark's Hospital, former Maidenhead Union Workhouse

29 Hungerford Hospital, former Hungerford Union Workhouse - closed in 1989, sold and later demolished

30 Sandleford Hospital, former Newbury Union Workhouse

31 Wayland Hospital, former Bradfield Union Workhouse - closed in 1991, sold and later demolished

32 St Mary's Hospital, former Wallingford Union Workhouse - closed in 1985, sold and later demolished

33 Townlands Hospital, former Henley Union Workhouse

34 Battle Hospital, former Reading Union Workhouse

* Indicates no illustrations available

VOLUNTARY GENERAL HOSPITALS
The Royal Berkshire Hospital, Reading

The Royal Berkshire Hospital, Reading was opened in 1839 on a 4 acre site given by Lord Sidmouth. Queen Victoria was the Patron. The 50 bed hospital, designed by Reading architect Henry Briant, was built and equipped at a cost of £13,000 and paid for by donations. The hospital was maintained entirely through voluntary contributions and subscriptions. Patients were admitted by ticket on the recommendation of a subscriber and attended by the honorary medical staff of surgeons and physicians. By 1947 the hospital had 461 beds and many specialist departments. In 2000, with 760 beds and now part of the Royal Berkshire and Battle Hospitals NHS Trust, further expansion is taking place to enable Battle Hospital facilities to be transferred to the one site.

1. The Royal Berkshire Hospital 1839.

2. The Royal Berkshire Hospital 1865.

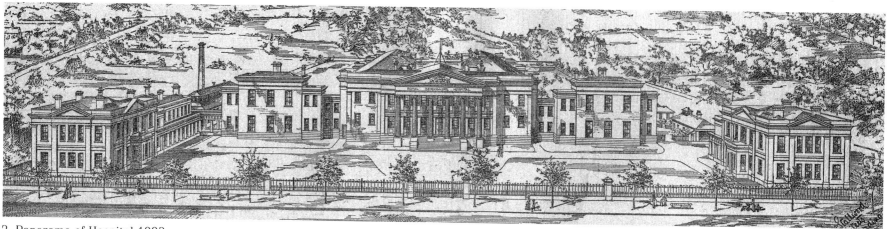

3. Panorama of Hospital 1883.

4. Medical and Nursing Staff c1880.

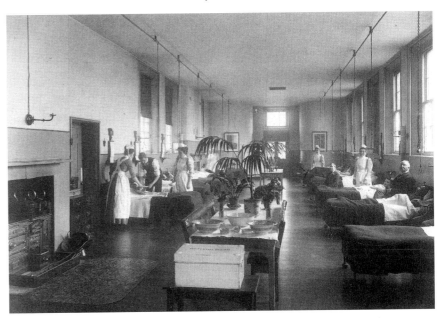

5. Benyon Ward 1900.

6. Front of Hospital c1880.

7. Matron's Sitting-room 1900.

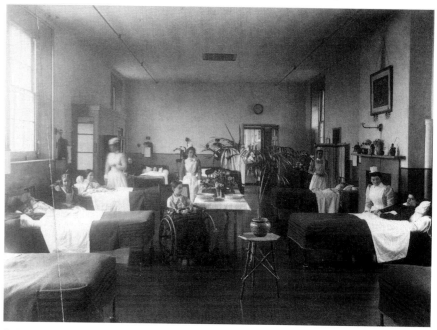

8. Victoria Ward 1900.

9. Children's Ward 1900.

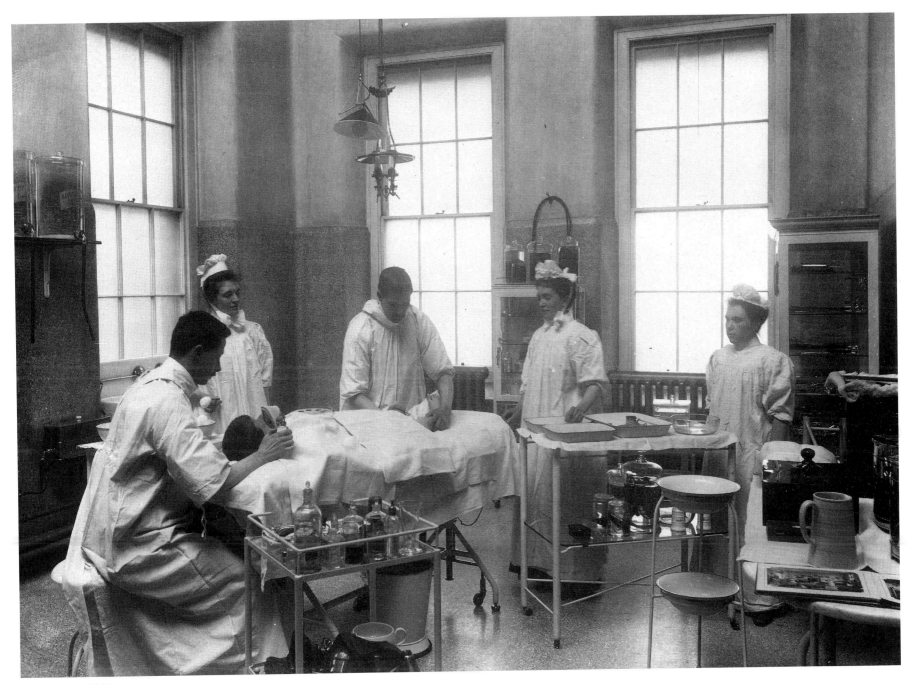

10. Theatre 1900.

11. King Edward VII Ward - the new Children's Ward - 1912.

12. Dispensary 1912.

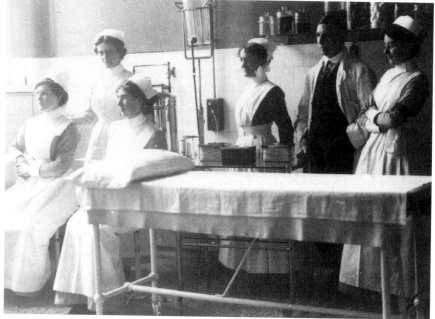

13. New Eye Theatre 1912.

14. X-ray Room 1917.

15. Pathological Laboratory 1922.

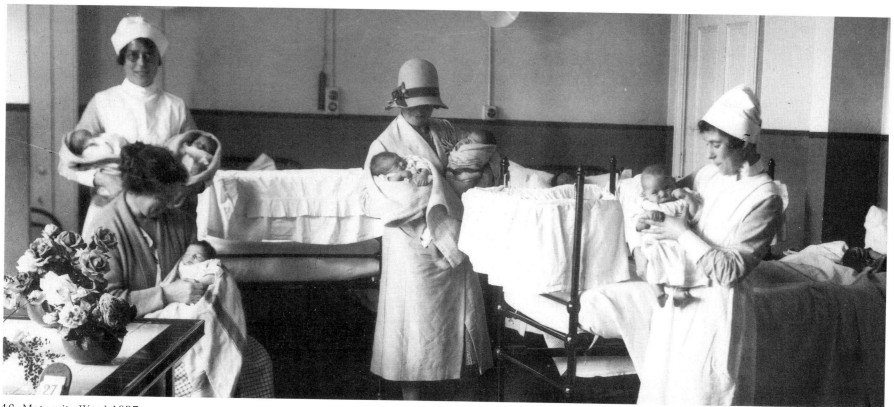

16. Maternity Ward 1927.

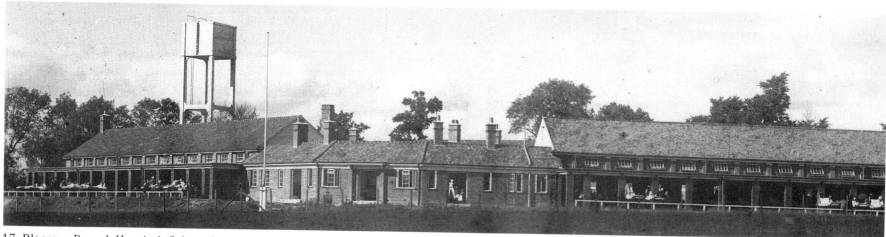

17. Blagrave Branch Hospital, Calcot. Opened 1930 with 60 beds. Originally for long-term treatment of non-pulmonary TB cases. Closed 1989 and sold for building.

Maidenhead General Hospital

This hospital was opened in 1879 as a cottage hospital with beds for 8 patients. The building, paid for by donations, was designed by Arthur Cooper and cost £2,400 to erect and equip. The hospital was maintained by voluntary donations and subscriptions. Patients were admitted by ticket on the recommendation of a subscriber. Additional accommodation was soon required and the hospital expanded to provide theatre, X-ray and other facilities. In 1920 the name was altered to Maidenhead General Hospital, often referred to locally as St Luke's Hospital. In 1947 there were 104 beds. In 1977, now with 100 beds, the hospital was closed and its services transferred to St Mark's Hospital, Maidenhead. The buildings were then demolished and houses built on the site.

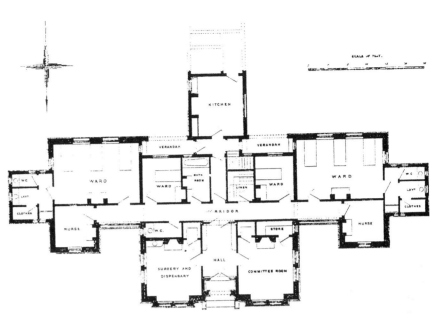

18. Plan of Maidenhead Hospital 1879.

19. Maidenhead Hospital 1915.

Newbury District Hospital

Newbury District Hospital, on the Andover Road, was opened in 1885 with 12 beds. The building was designed by architect HG Turner and cost £2,400 to erect and equip. The hospital was built and maintained by voluntary donations and subscriptions. Patients were admitted on the recommendation of a subscriber and attended by an honorary medical staff. Those who were able to do so were asked to contribute towards their cost. The hospital rapidly expanded and by 1947 had 90 beds treating both acute and general cases. In 2000, with 48 beds it is part of the West Berkshire Priority Care Services NHS Trust. Plans are underway to replace this hospital with a new one on a different site in the area.

20. Newbury District Hospital 1885.

21. Newbury District Hospital 1908.

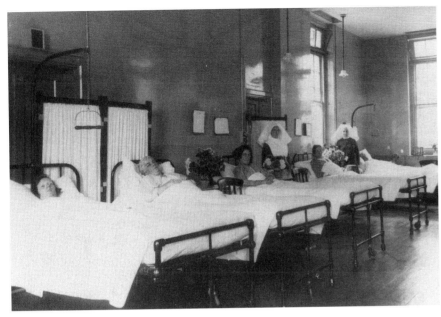

22. Women's Ward 1930.

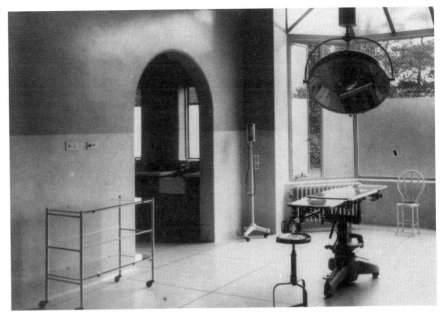

24. Theatre 1930.

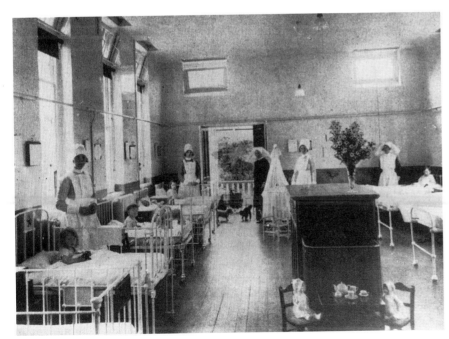

23. Children's Ward 1930.

25. Newbury District Hospital 1930.

King Edward VII Hospital, Windsor

King Edward VII Hospital was opened in 1909 as the successor to the Windsor Dispensary and Infirmary. The innovative steel-framed building was designed by architect AW West. The £25,000 required to build and equip the 50 bed hospital was raised mainly by donations. King Edward was the hospital's Patron. The hospital was maintained by subscriptions and donations. Patients were admitted on the recommendation of a subscriber and attended by an honorary medical staff. Greatly enlarged over the years, by 1947 the hospital had 199 beds. In 2000 it is now part of the East Berkshire Community Health NHS Trust. The building has recently undergone extensive alterations to improve the many out-patient facilities and the Prince Charles Eye Unit.

26. Foundation Stone Ceremony June 22 1908.

27. Building nearing completion. Opened March 1909.

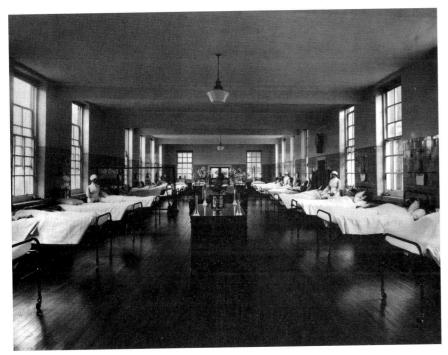

28. King Edward VII Ward 1909.

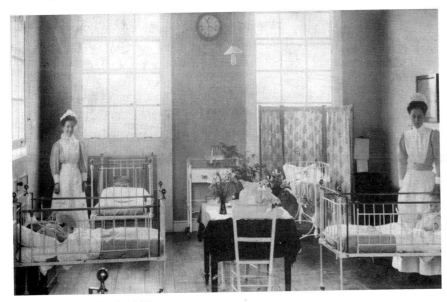

29. Children's Ward 1909.

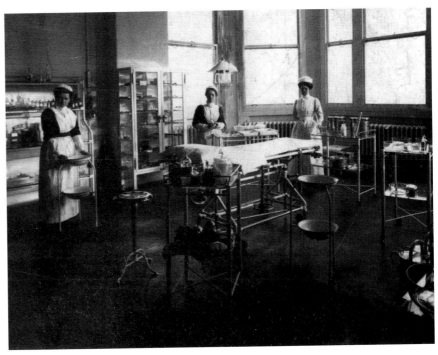

30. Theatre 1909.

31. Out-patients' Waiting Room 1909.

32. Group of Hospital Nurses.

33. Laboratory.

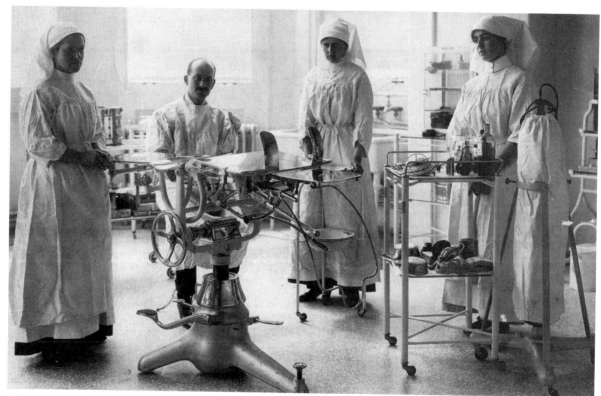

34. Theatre c1915.

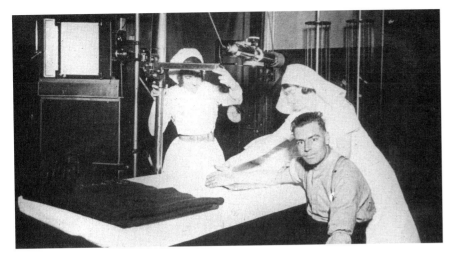

35. X-ray Department.

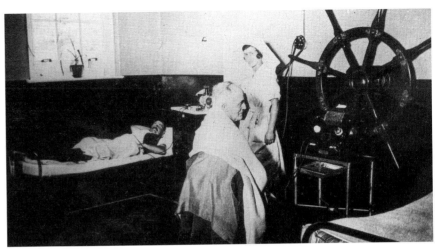

37. Electrical Treatment.

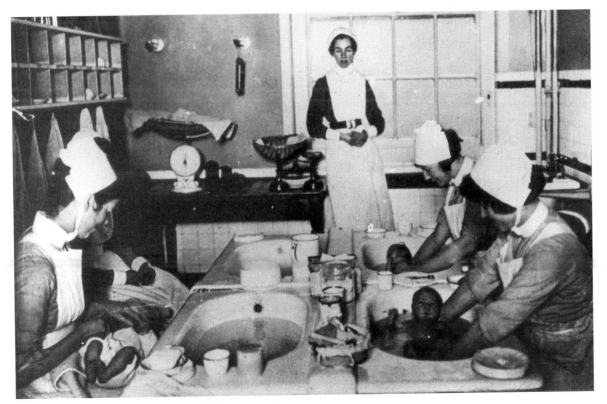

36. Bathing babies in the Maternity Department.

COTTAGE HOSPITALS

Speen Cottage Hospital

Speen Cottage Hospital was opened in 1869 with 6 beds in a building designed by James Money. The idea of a cottage hospital, the first in the area, was promoted by the Revd HW Majendie, Vicar of Speen, who gave the land and paid for the building. He became its first patient when he was admitted with a broken leg and subsequently died on December 17 1869. The hospital was equipped through voluntary contributions and maintained largely through subscriptions and donations. Patients, admitted on the recommendation of a subscriber, were asked to make modest weekly payments. By 1912 it had become a convalescent home, still with 6 beds. In 1946, just before the advent of the NHS, the Trustees closed the home and sold the property. The money raised was used to endow the Majendie Charity for the Poor of Speen.

Wallingford Cottage Hospital

The Wallingford Cottage Hospital, designed by JS Dodd, was opened in 1881 on a site in the London Road given by Mr Hawkins, Mayor of Wallingford. The hospital, with 8 beds, cost £1,155 to build, practically all of which was donated by Mr and Mrs Herbert Morrell. In its early years it was known as the Morrell Cottage Hospital. It was funded by voluntary donations and subscriptions. The patients were attended by an honorary medical staff. In 1929 the hospital was transferred to a new building on the London Road and in 1947 it had 17 beds. In 1972 the hospital was extended and in the following year became the Wallingford Community Hospital.

38. Speen Cottage Hospital.

39. Wallingford Cottage Hospital c1908.

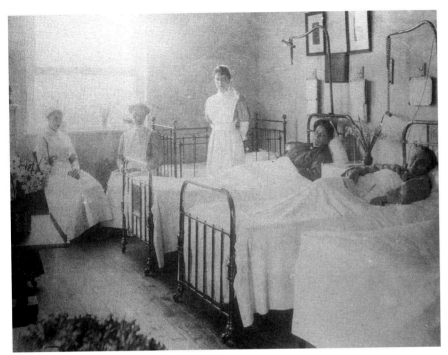

40. Women's Ward c1906.

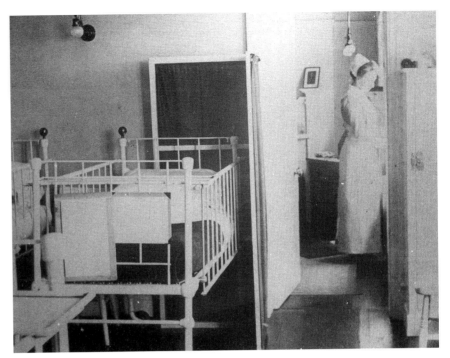

41. Children's Ward.

42. New Cottage Hospital 1929.

The Royal Victoria Cottage Hospital, South Ascot

The Royal Victoria Cottage Hospital, South Ascot was opened in 1898 to mark Queen Victoria's Diamond Jubilee. Dean Liddell and Mrs Liddell of Ascot Wood (parents of Alice in Wonderland) were instrumental in its concept, gave the land and were among the many local people who raised the £2,338 to build and equip the hospital. It had 9 beds, an operating theatre and accommodation for 7 nurses. It was funded by voluntary contributions. In 1947 the hospital had 12 beds. It was later used as a training school and nurses' home for Heatherwood Hospital after which it was used to accommodate Heatherwood staff. It was subsequently sold and the land used for building.

Henley War Memorial Hospital

Henley War Memorial Hospital was built as a memorial to the 339 local men killed in the First World War. The 2 acre site, on the outskirts of the town, was given by Mr John C Walker whose son was killed at Gallipoli in 1915. The building, designed by Charles S Smith of Reading, was paid for and equipped through public donations. It was opened in 1923 with 8 beds in 2 public wards, 3 private wards, a theatre, X-ray room, rooms for staff, a laundry, garage and mortuary. By 1947 it had expanded to provide 17 beds. In 1984 it was closed and later sold for redevelopment.

43. Royal Victoria Cottage Hospital c 1900.

44. Henley War Memorial Hospital 1920s.

45. Opening ceremony.

46. Hospital with later addition.

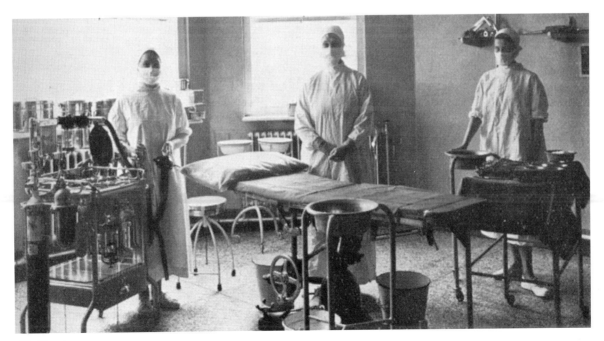

47. Theatre.

MENTAL HOSPITALS
Broadmoor Hospital, Crowthorne

Broadmoor Hospital, in grounds of 290 acres, was opened as a criminal lunatic asylum in 1863. The building was designed by General Sir Joshua Jebb KCB, the architect of Pentonville Prison, and built using labour from Parkhurst Prison in the Isle of Wight. The completed hospital had beds for 500 patients. The buildings covered some 18 acres and originally comprised seven blocks with wards, airing courts, workshops, offices and a chapel. In the grounds were three houses and 57 cottages for staff, a school with accommodation for teachers and also farm buildings for the 167 acre farm. Many changes and alterations have been made over the years. Since 1948 the hospital has been part of the NHS. In 2000 the hospital has 430 patients and is administered by the Broadmoor Hospital Authority.

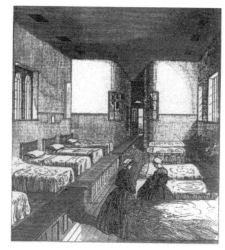

48. Female dormitory 1864.

49. Male dormitory 1864.

50. General view of Hospital 1864.

51. Original entrance to Hospital.

52. Broadmoor Staff 1885.

53. Female Wing Staff c1920.

Berkshire County Mental Hospital

Also known as the Moulsford Asylum or Fair Mile Hospital, the Berkshire County Mental Hospital was opened in 1870 in the parish of Cholsey to receive patients from Berkshire and also those who had previously been admitted to the Littlemore Asylum in Oxford (opened in 1847). The building, designed by CH Howell and built in 80 acres of land, cost £68,500 and could accommodate 285 patients. Many alterations and extensions were made over the years and by 1947 there were 964 beds. By 2000, now part of the West Berkshire Priority Care Services NHS Trust, the number of patients had fallen considerably. It is planned to close the hospital and build a smaller, more suitable and convenient building at Prospect Park in Reading due to open in 2002.

54. Berkshire County Mental Hospital 1880.

55. Berkshire County Mental Hospital 1870.

Borocourt Hospital

In 1930 Wyfold Court, an imposing Victorian Gothic mansion, was purchased by the local authorities of Buckinghamshire, Berkshire, Reading and Oxfordshire to use as a hospital for mental defectives. The house was built in the 1870s for Edward Hermon, MP for Preston, and designed by architect George Somers Clarke a pupil of Sir Charles Barry. Renamed Borocourt Hospital, by 1947 the building, with many extensions in the grounds, could accommodate 400 patients. In 1993 the hospital was closed and the mansion, now listed graded II*, was sold. By 2000 the house had been converted into flats and houses built in the grounds.

56. Berkshire County Mental Hospital Staff c1900.

57. Berkshire County Mental Hospital Staff c1920.

58. Borocourt Hospital.

TUBERCULOSIS SANATORIUMS
Peppard Sanatorium

Peppard Sanatorium was founded in 1898 by Dr Esther Carling to provide open-air treatment for patients suffering from pulmonary tuberculosis. From a modest beginning in Kingswood Farmhouse and with the addition of Maitland House (built in 1910) the sanatorium rapidly expanded. In 1914 Dr Carling sold the sanitorium, which now had 70 beds, with its 50 acre farm to the Berkshire and Buckinghamshire County Councils but remained as the Resident Medical Officer. The administrative body was now the Berks and Bucks Joint Sanatorium Committee. In 1947 there were 260 beds but in the following years, as the number of TB patients declined with the advent of antibiotics, other chest diseases and later heart diseases were treated and the hospital eventually became known as Peppard Hospital. The hospital was gradually closed during the 1980s and was later sold with the land for building.

59. Kingswood Farmhouse 1907.

60. Maitland Sanatorium c1910.

61. Peppard Farm and buildings.

63. Kindercot for children.

62. Group of patients and staff.

64. Rotating open-air chalets.

Pinewood Sanatorium

Pinewood Sanatorium was built by the London County Council in 1901 at a cost of £40,000 in grounds of 82 acres off Nine Mile Ride in Wokingham. It provided open-air treatment for patients with pulmonary tuberculosis coming from the London area. In 1919 it had beds for 160 patients. In 1948 it became part of the NHS and was administered by the North-West Metropolitan Regional Hospital Board. When the number of TB patients declined the hospital specialised in chest diseases including cancer. The hospital closed in 1966 and in 1973 the site and buildings were purchased by Wokingham Rural District Council. In 2000 part has been developed as a leisure centre and the remainder taken over by Hewlett-Packard.

65. Main entrance.

66. South front.

67. General view.

69. Open-air huts.

68. Balconies.

70. The Green Walk.

CHILDREN'S HOSPITALS
Cold Ash Children's Hospital

Founded in 1886 by Miss Bowditch in her home at Cold Ash, this hospital treated poor children who required skilled nursing combined with country air. In 1892 a new building with 20 beds, designed by architect JH Money, was opened and in 1897 Princess Christian became the Patron. Children with a variety of illnesses ranging from non-pulmonary TB to infantile paralysis were admitted from London hospitals, the Children's Aid Association and all parts of Berkshire. As most cases were long-stay patients, a teacher was employed to continue their education. The hospital was funded by subscriptions and donations and those not admitted on a subscriber's ticket were asked to pay 7/- (35p) a week. In 1947 the hospital had 36 beds for long-stay patients. It was closed in 1963 and sold for building.

71. Cold Ash Children's Hospital 1892.

72. Cold Ash Children's Hospital 1913.

Heatherwood Hospital, Ascot

Heatherwood Hospital was opened in 1923 in the grounds of a former mansion of that name. It was built and maintained by the Council of Management of the United Services Fund. This fund was established after the 1914-18 war with the profits from the Expeditionary Force Canteen and from funds from disbanded army units. It was to be used for the benefit of ex-servicemen and their dependants. Heatherwood Hospital opened with 136 beds to provide treatment for ex-servicemen's children suffering from surgical tuberculosis and other orthopaedic diseases. In 1934 the hospital was given to the London County Council to secure its funding. Children from London would be admitted with priority given to children of ex-servicemen. After the advent of the NHS it became a general hospital serving the Bracknell area. In 2000, with 266 beds and greatly extended facilities, it forms part of the Heatherwood and Wexham Park Hospitals Trust.

74. Heatherwood Hospital c1923.

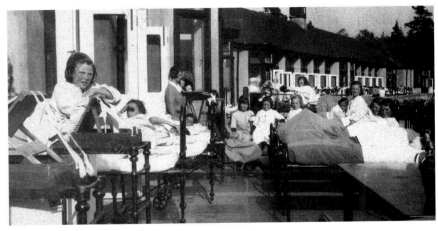

75. Open-air School.

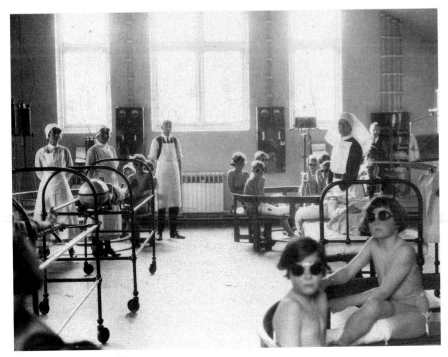

73. Artificial Light Treatment.

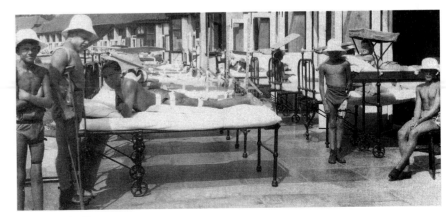

76. Sunlight Treatment.

CONVALESCENT HOSPITALS
London and Ascot Convalescent Hospital

This hospital, also known as Ascot Priory, was the inspiration of Priscilla Lydia Sellon, founder of the Society of the Most Holy Trinity, Devonport, supported by Dr Edward Pewsey. A 40 acre site was purchased near Ascot in 1860 and the convalescent hospital with 50 beds, built to the design of Charles Buckeridge, was opened in 1863. The site and building cost £10,000. Convalescents were admitted regardless of creed and nursed by the Sisters. The hospital was maintained by subscriptions and payments for patients. The original hospital consisted of a splendid 100 foot ward with rooms for the Sisters. The Princess of Wales became the Patron. Additions were made to the building including a south wing in 1902. Financial constraints prevented further expansion and in 1947 there were 53 beds. Subsequently the hospital became a private nursing home.

77. Ascot Priory.

78. Ascot Priory.

79. Hospital.

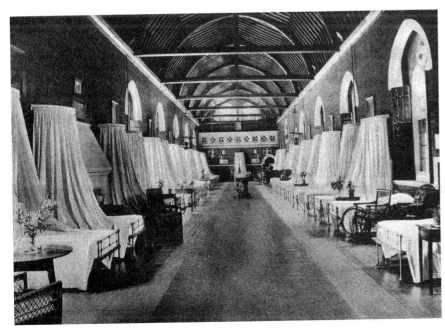

80. London and Ascot Convalescent Hospital Ward.

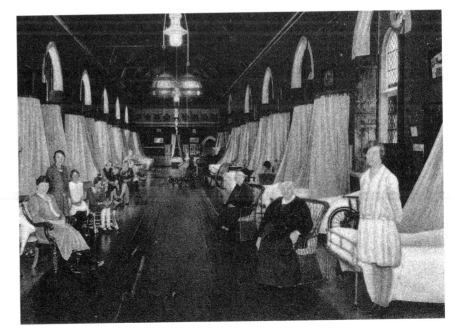

81. Hospital Ward.

St Andrew's Convalescent Hospital, Clewer

St Andrew's Convalescent Hospital was opened in 1866 with 64 beds on a site belonging to and adjoining the Convent of St John the Baptist in Clewer. The building, designed by architect Henry Woodyer, cost £12,000 to build. Queen Victoria was the Patron. The hospital was maintained by voluntary contributions and staffed by the Sisters of the Convent. No surgical cases were admitted and patients were attended by honorary physicians. Those who could afford to do so were asked to contribute towards their keep. The hospital expanded to 81 beds and remained open until the 1939-1945 war when it was requisitioned as a nurses' hostel. When Newton Court was opened for the nurses in Old Windsor the hospital was returned to the Sisters. It proved impossible to maintain after the War and in 1954 the building was demolished and houses erected on the site.

82. St Andrew's Hospital c1900.

83. St Andrew's Hospital 1866.

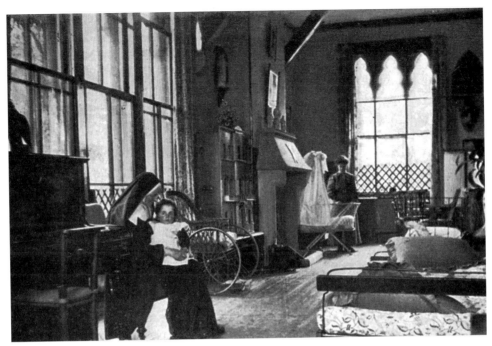
84. Children's Ward c1900.

85. Men's Ward c1900.

86. St Cross Ward for women.

PRIVATE NURSES AND DISTRICT NURSES
Royal Berkshire Hospital Private Nurses

In 1873 a private nursing scheme was inaugurated at the hospital whereby nurses trained at the hospital would be available to nurse private families at a set scale of charges. This service was extended in 1875 and offered either free or at a reduced rate to the poor of the area. Medical and surgical cases were charged 1 guinea per week, fever cases £1-11-6d and mental cases £2-2/- per week. By 1890 some 28 nurses were employed in the scheme and by 1901 this had increased to 34. In 1921 a set fee of 3 guineas per week was charged. In 1940 it became impracticable to continue the scheme in wartime and the Private Nursing Department was closed.

87. Royal Berkshire Hospital Private Nurses c1895.

Private Nurse

REGULATIONS FOR PRIVATE NURSING.

The rate of remuneration for attendance of the Nurse is in ordinary cases £1 1s. 0d. per week or part of week ; travelling expenses and washing to be paid by the family employing the Nurse. If the case is infectious, the charge is £1 11s. 6d. per week. As a rule, mental cases are not undertaken, but if a Nurse is sent to one, or if an ordinary case become such whilst under the care of a Nurse, £2 2s. 0d. per week is charged.

For short and special attendance, as on operations or the like, special charges are made according to circumstances.

After four weeks, if it be wished to retain the Nurse, a communication to that effect should be addressed to the Lady Superintendent.

It is particularly requested—

1.—That no gratuity in money or clothing be offered to the Nurse. A book or other article of small value, as a token of remembrance from a patient, may, however, be accepted by a Nurse. Or should it be desired to acknowledge in a special manner the services rendered by the Nurse, a gift may be made towards the Nurses' Reward Fund for those who have served many years or become disabled.

2.—That no Wine or Spirits be given to the Nurse unless at the request of the Medical Attendant.

3.—That, if possible, the Nurse be allowed to rest every third night ; and that when her services are needed for several consecutive nights, she be allowed at least eight hours' rest in each day out of the sick room.

4.—That when the Nurse's services are no longer required, a report may be returned to the Lady Superintendent, sealed, with a candid statement of her conduct and efficiency, either from one of the family or the Medical Attendant, and that 24 hours' notice be given of her return to the Hospital.

5.—Any misconduct on the part of the Nurse should without delay be communicated to the Lady Superintendent.

6.—All money for the services of the nurses to be paid monthly to the Lady Superintendent, Royal Berkshire Hospital.

It is hoped that contributions to the General Nursing Fund may be made, as Nurses are supplied to the poor gratuitously, or to those in straitened circumstances at a reduced charge, and it is earnestly hoped that the liberality of the wealthy may enable the Institution to extend this very important part of its work.

88. Rules for Royal Berkshire Hospital Private Nurses.

89. Private Nurse at Sulham House 1912.

Queen Victoria Nurses

In 1887 the Queen Victoria Institute of Nursing was founded to mark Her Majesty's Golden Jubilee. This enabled a fund to be established for the training of nurses to visit the poor in their own homes In 1897 the Queen Victoria Institute for Nursing the Sick Poor of Reading was founded to mark the Queen's Diamond Jubilee. Premises were obtained at Abbots Walk and nurses were made available to attend cases in the area. The formation of the Berkshire County Nursing Association in 1905 extended the work of district nurses and midwives and many local nursing associations were affiliated to both the Queen's Institute and the County Association. In 1948 the County Council took over the services previously given by the Institute and the County Association.

90. Queen Victoria Institute Nurses in Reading c1900.

91. Queen Victoria Institute Nurses outside their Abbots Walk Headquarters, Reading.

Princess Christian Nurses

Princess Christian, Queen Victoria's third daughter married to Prince Christian of Schleswig-Holstein, was an active supporter of the role of district nurses. In 1886 she inaugurated a scheme whereby trained nurses, called Princess Christian Nurses, would be available to nurse the poor of Windsor and the neighbourhood. The nurses were based at a house in Clarence Villas. Affiliation with the Queen Victoria Institute of Nursing was obtained. The scheme was most successful and twenty years later 4 district nurses, 2 midwives and 31 private nurses were employed. Larger premises were obtained which eventually became the Princess Christian Nursing Home.

92. Princess Christian Nurses in Windsor c1900.

ISOLATION HOSPITALS

The need to isolate patients with infectious diseases was recognised from early times. By the early 20th century most parishes had access to isolation hospitals which had been built in place of former temporary arrangements. At the Royal Berkshire Hospital, Reading, a special building designed by Joseph Morris, was opened in 1878 to isolate patients who developed infectious illnesses while in hospital. Isolation hospitals for infectious diseases other than smallpox were built at Newbury (Wash Common), Hungerford, Maidenhead, Wallingford, Henley (Smith Hospital), Cippenham and Reading. All were built by local authorities and paid for out of the rates.

94. A fully equipped temporary tent hospital was erected in Clewer in 1893 to receive patients during a severe smallpox epidemic. There was no isolation hospital at that time.

93. Wallingford Isolation Hospital opened in1904 with corrugated iron wards for 11 patients and a brick administration building designed by WR Howell. Further additions were made and in 1947 the hospital had 34 beds. The corrugated iron buildings were demolished and the brick buildings used for maternity cases until the Community Hospital was opened in 1973. The building was demolished in the mid-1980s and houses built on the site.

95. Maidenhead Isolation Hospital. The third to be built on the site. In 1893 an iron building with 8 beds was erected in addition to earlier wooden huts. Between 1909 and 1930 the hospital was gradually enlarged and the earlier buildings replaced by permanent brick buildings. By 1948 it had 54 beds. In 1978 it was no longer used as an isolation hospital and took respite care cases from St Mark's Hospital opposite. Closed in 1984 and sold for building.

96. Hungerford Isolation Hospital. Ward during First World War. This small single storey building of timber clad with corrugated iron was demolished in 1940s.

97. Cippenham Isolation Hospital 1918. Built in early 1900s to serve the Windsor area. By 1920 it had been rebuilt and enlarged. In 1947 it had 62 beds. Closed early 1950s.

98. A ward for infectious cases at the Royal Berkshire Hospital c1925. The two ward building is now used for offices.

99. Park Hospital, Reading. Built by the Borough Council in 1906. Designed by Charles Smith on a 10 acre site with 40 beds for scarlet fever and diphtheria patients. By 1947 it had expanded to provide 104 beds, 26 of which were for TB cases. It closed to patients in 1987 and in 1988 became the administrative headquarters of the West Berkshire Health Authority. In 2000 it has been earmarked as the site for the new hospital in place of Fair Mile Hospital.

100. View of Park Hospital Hospital pavilions.

102. Scarlet Fever and Diphtheria pavilion.

101. Part of Hospital.

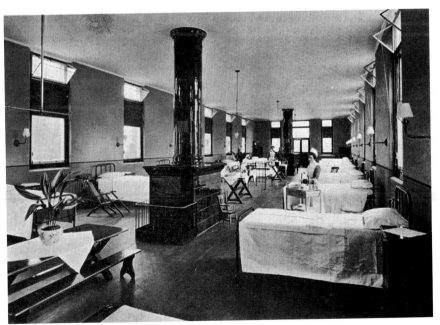

103. Scarlet Fever Ward.

WORKHOUSE INFIRMARIES

104. Eton Union Workhouse c1890. Built in 1836 for 300 paupers. Designed by Kempthorne. In 1840 a 30 bed infirmary designed by Sargeant was added. In 1930 it became a Public Assistance Institution and during the 1939-45 war Emergency Medical Service beds were added. In 1947 there were 191 PAI beds and 200 EMS beds.

105. Windsor Union Workhouse c1920. Built in 1840 for 282 paupers. Architects Scott and Moffatt. An infirmary with 50 beds was added later. In 1930 it became a Public Assistance Institution. During the 1939-45 war Emergency Medical Service beds were added and the hospital extended its services. In 1947 there were 167 PAI beds and 199 EMS beds.

106. Bradfield Union Workhouse c1920. Built in 1835, designed by Kempthorne. New infirmary designed by Scott and Moffatt built in 1842. In 1930 it became a Public Assistance Institution.

107. Wallingford Union Workhouse. In 1835 the former parish workhouse was enlarged with additions designed by Plowman of Oxford. In 1930 it became a Public Assistance Institution and in 1947 it had 117 beds for the chronic sick.

109. Wokingham Union Workhouse 1900. Built in 1850, designed by Billing of Reading. In 1930 it became a Public Assistance Institution and in 1947 it had 111 beds for the chronic sick.

108. Newbury Union Workhouse Master and Matron and Nursing Staff 1910. This workhouse, designed by Kempthorne, was built in 1836. An infirmary designed by J. Hanson of Speenhamland was added in 1837. It became a Public Assistance Institution in 1930 and in 1947 had 111 beds for the chronic sick.

110. Wokingham Union Workhouse c1920.

111. Reading Union Workhouse c1890. A new workhouse with an infirmary was built in 1867 on an 8.5 acre site. Designed by Reading architect William Woodman, it cost some £14,000 to build.

114. Nursing Staff 1911. By 1911, the workhouse had a training school for nurses and was considered one of the most up-to-date in the country.

112. Extensions designed by Charles Smith of Reading between 1889 and 1892 included a new 185 bed infirmary.

113. Further extensions in 1911 included a new theatre.

115. In 1930 the infirmary became a municipal hospital called Battle Hospital, and the former workhouse accommodation became a Public Assistance Institution to care for the elderly and chronic sick.

Former Workhouses Update

In 1948 the 11 former workhouses in the present Berkshire and South Oxfordshire area became NHS hospitals. By 2000 three had been sold for building and demolished and one had been sold and converted into flats.

117. Windsor Union Workhouse after 1948 became known as Old Windsor Hospital and was closely connected with King Edward VII Hospital. It closed in 1988 and the building was sold and converted into flats.

116. Henley Union Workhouse previously the Poor House built in 1790 with later additions, was called Townlands Hospital after 1948 and expanded its services. In 2000 it is part of the West Berkshire Priority Care Services NHS Trust and provides 15 beds for young disabled patients and 20 medical/rehabilitation beds run by GPs, There is also a 24 hour nurse-led minor injuries unit, outpatient clinics for most specialties, facilities for the elderly and those with mental health and learning disabilities.

118. Eton Union Workhouse after 1948 was called Upton Hospital. In 2000 it is a community hospital with 105 beds and forms part of the East Berkshire Community Health NHS Trust.

119. Easthampstead Union Workhouse after 1948 was called Church Hill House Hospital. In 2000 it cares for patients with learning disabilities and is administered by the East Berkshire NHS Trust. The building is scheduled for demolition.

120. Wokingham Union Workhouse after 1948 was called Wokingham Hospital and expanded its services. In 2000 it provides 32 beds for rehabilitation of the elderly and a wide range of outpatient facilities. It is part of the West Berkshire Priority Care Services NHS Trust.

121. Maidenhead Union Workhouse built in 1836. After 1948 it was called St Mark's Hospital and expanded its services. In 2000 it has a 25 bed GP ward and a 25 bed elderly mentally impaired ward as well as outpatient clinics for most specialties, a Day Hospital for the elderly and a Children's Centre. It is part of the East Berkshire Community Health NHS Trust.

122. Hungerford Union Workhouse, built in 1847, was called Hungerford Hospital after 1948. It closed in 1989, was sold and later demolished and houses built on the site.

123. Newbury Union Workhouse. After 1948 became known as Sandleford Hospital and expanded its services. In 1995 the front of the building was demolished. In 2000 it has 24 beds for elderly rehabilitation patients and also antenatal and physiotherapy outpatient facilities. It is part of the West Berkshire Priority Care Services NHS Trust.

124. Bradfield Union Workhouse was known as Wayland Hospital after 1948. It closed in 1991, the buildings were sold and later demolished and houses built on the site.

125. Wallingford Union Workhouse. After 1948 was called St Mary's Hospital and expanded its services. It closed in 1985. The building was sold and later demolished and houses built on the site.

126. Battle Hospital former Reading Union Workhouse. In 1948, with 384 beds, it became a general hospital under the NHS and expanded to provide many specialist services. In 1972 the new Abbey Building was opened. In 2000, with 280 beds, it is part of the Royal Berkshire and Battle Hospitals NHS Trust. Work is underway to transfer its services to the Royal Berkshire Hospital site.

FIRST WORLD WAR HOSPITALS

In March 1915 the War Office commandeered the Reading Union Workhouse and within six weeks converted the buildings into a 400 bed military hospital, known as the Reading War Hospital. During the following six months four fully equipped section hospitals were opened in nearby schools. These were known collectively as the Reading War Hospital and numbered 1 to 5. The Reading Union Workhouse now became known as No. 1 (Central) War Hospital. In the meantime the Royal Berkshire Hospital, Newbury District Hospital and Maidenhead General Hospital had opened military wards and King Edward VII Hospital followed in 1916. Auxiliary hospitals, equipped and staffed by the British Red Cross Society, opened throughout the area. Most were affiliated to the Reading War Hospital. Across the county border in Taplow, HRH Duchess of Connaught Hospital, a 600 bed hutted hospital, was opened in the grounds of Lord Astor's estate at Cliveden. Maidenhead Auxiliary Hospital was affiliated to the Cliveden hospital.

127. Entrance to the Reading War Hospital 1915.

128. Former workhouse infirmary became part of Reading War Hospital.

129. Patients on roof of C Block.

130. Ward in F Block.

131. Electrical Department.

132. No.2 War Hospital at Battle School. Opened July 1915 with 200 beds.

133. No.3 War Hospital at Wilson School. Opened September 1915 with 300 beds.

134. No.4 War Hospital at Redlands School. Opened June 1915 with 180 beds.

135. Ward at No.4 War Hospital, Redlands School.

136. No.5 War Hospital at Katesgrove School. Opened September 1915 with 200 beds.

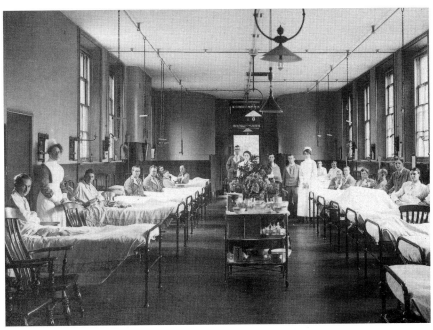

138. Royal Berkshire Hospital's first military ward (Benyon) opened 1914. The hospital provided 156 military beds by 1917.

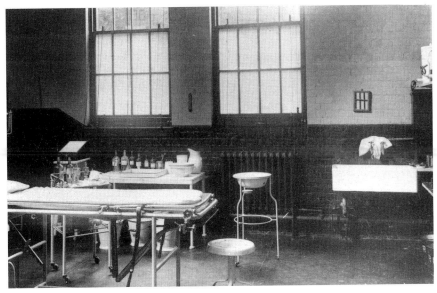

137. Theatre at No.5 War Hospital, Katesgrove School.

139. Marquee in grounds of Royal Berkshire Hospital 1915 following an outbreak of cerebro-spinal meningitis.

140. Military patients at Newbury District Hospital.

142. Private houses provided wards for military patients. The Gallery, Englefield House provided 25 beds.

141. Military patients at King Edward VII Hospital, Windsor.

143. Church Halls became Auxiliary Hospitals. St Luke's Hall, Reading provided 30 beds.

144. Maidenhead Technical Institute was taken over and opened in November 1914 with 200 beds.

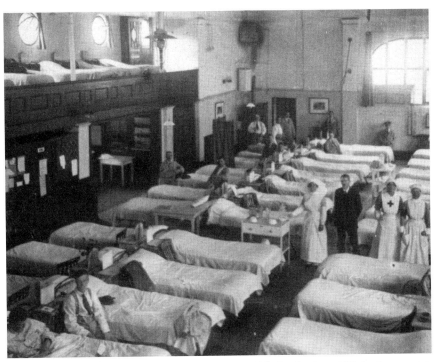

145. The Drill Hall adjoining the Institute provided a further 100 beds.

146. HRH Duchess of Connaught Hospital, Cliveden. A hutted hospital with 600 beds.

147/148. Large houses were rented and converted into auxiliary hospitals. Struan House, Reading opened in November 1914 with 77 beds.

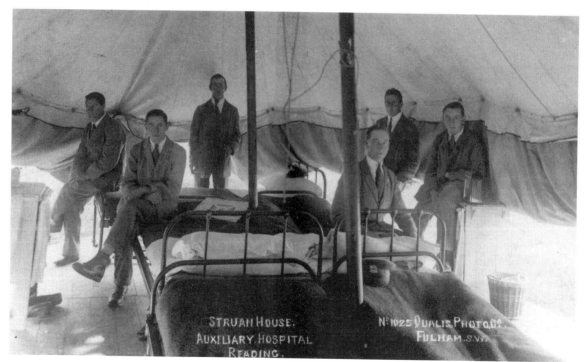

149. Interior of Marquee at Struan House, Reading.

150. Inniscarra, Reading opened March 1916 with 50 beds.

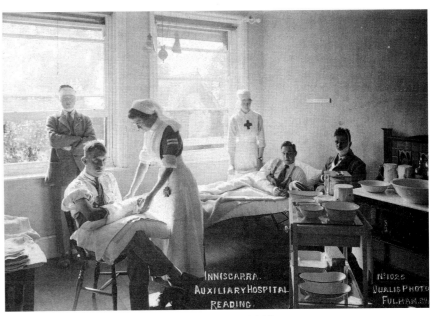

151. Interior of ward at Inniscarra, Reading 1918.

152. Medical and Nursing Staff at No.1(Central) Reading War Hospital 1918.